elbow
asleep in the back

Published 2001

Editorial & Production Anna Joyce
Folio Design Dominic Brookman
Music arranged & processed by Artemis Music Ltd Bucks SL0 0NH
Design by Five Feet Tall

Warner/Chappell Music Ltd
© International Music Publications Ltd
Griffin House 161 Hammersmith Road London England W6 8BS

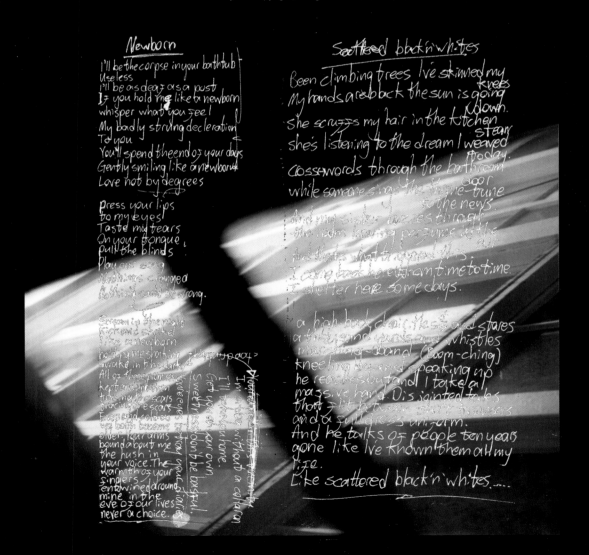

ANY DAY NOW

Words and Music by Guy Garvey, Mark Potter, Craig Potter,
Richard Jupp and Pete Turner

5

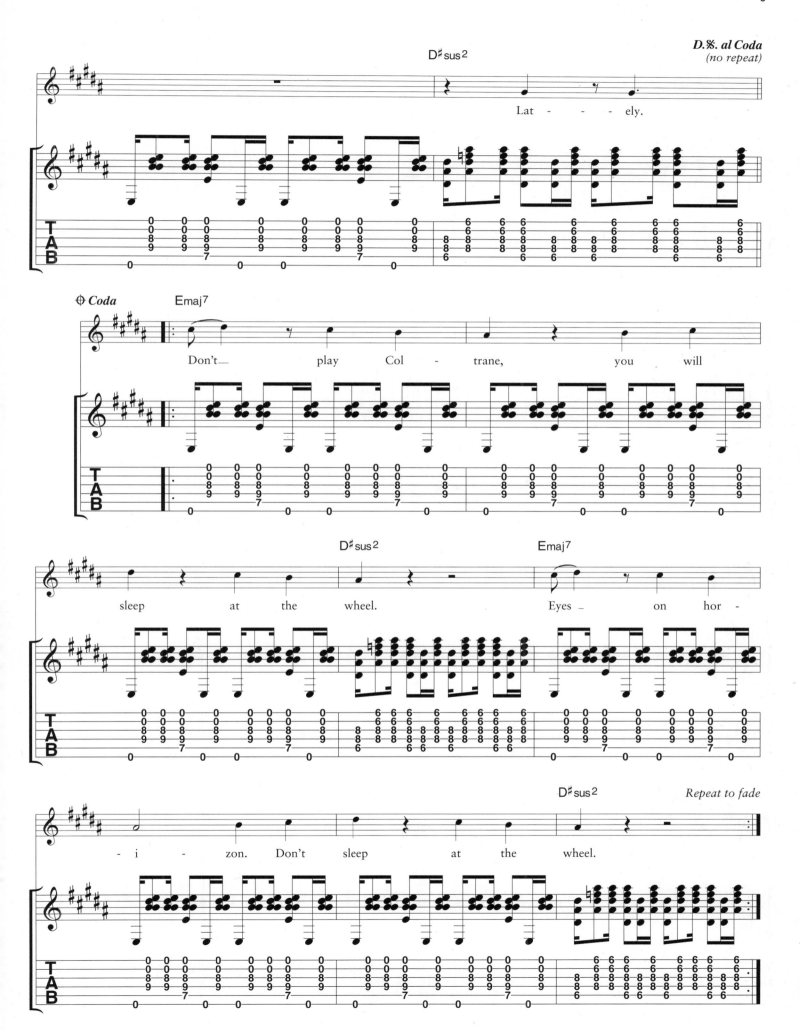

6

RED

Words and Music by Guy Garvey, Mark Potter, Craig Potter,
Richard Jupp and Pete Turner

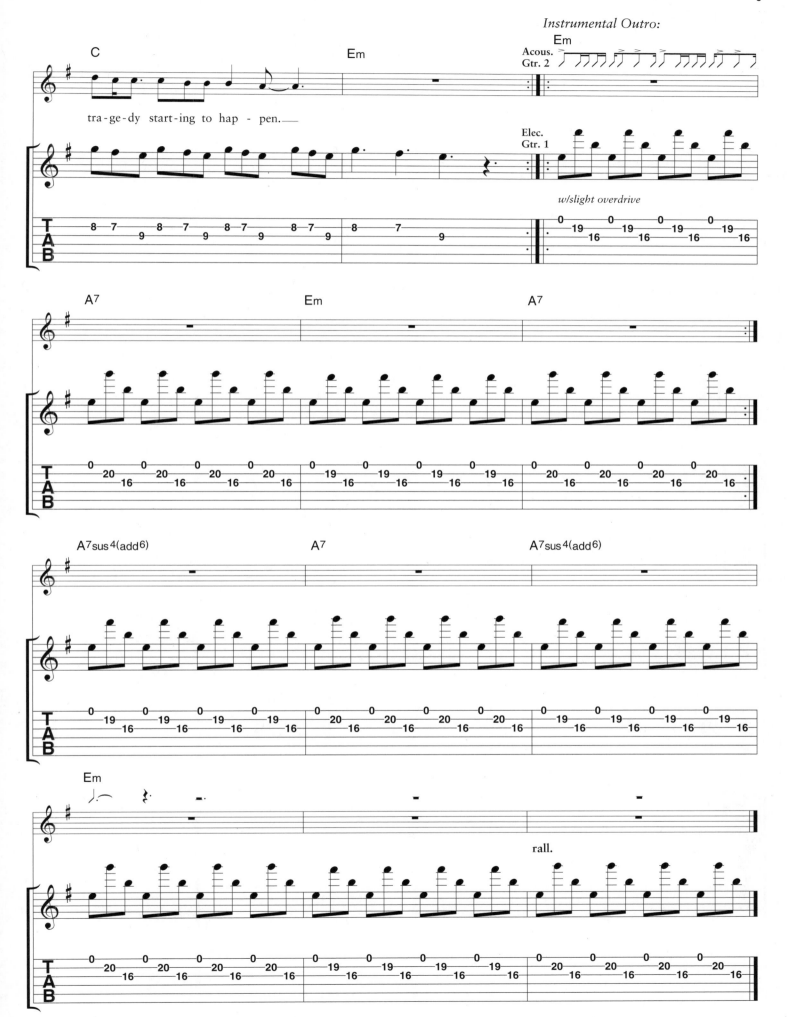

tra-ge-dy start-ing to hap - pen.

Instrumental Outro:

LITTLE BEAST

Words and Music by Guy Garvey, Mark Potter, Craig Potter,
Richard Jupp and Pete Turner

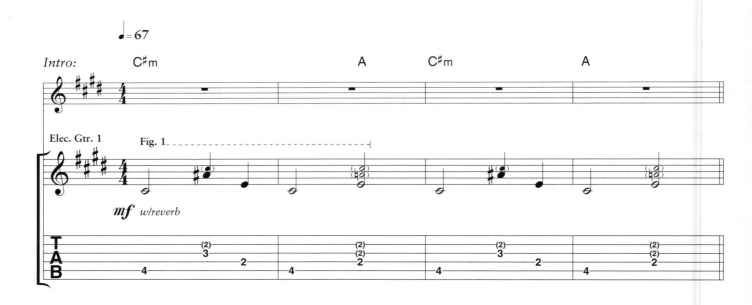

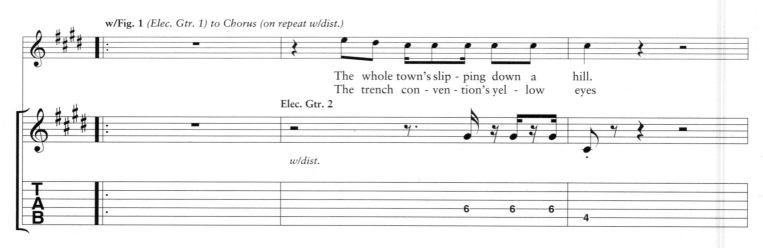

w/Fig. 2 (Elec. Gtr. 1) 4 times

Chorus:

(on repeat distortion off)

Burn your mark— and leave.—
Since bap - tism— per - ox - ide.—

Gtr. 2: ad lib. 2nd time

(Verse 1 tacet)
And fear is not re-spect, cor - rect. But it's the best— you're gon - na get.—

Sharp blow to the bridge of your nose. —

Fig. 2

Elec. Gtr. 1

POWDER BLUE

Words and Music by Guy Garvey, Mark Potter, Craig Potter,
Richard Jupp and Pete Turner

BITTEN BY THE TAIL FLY

Words and Music by Guy Garvey, Mark Potter, Craig Potter,
Richard Jupp and Pete Turner

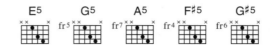

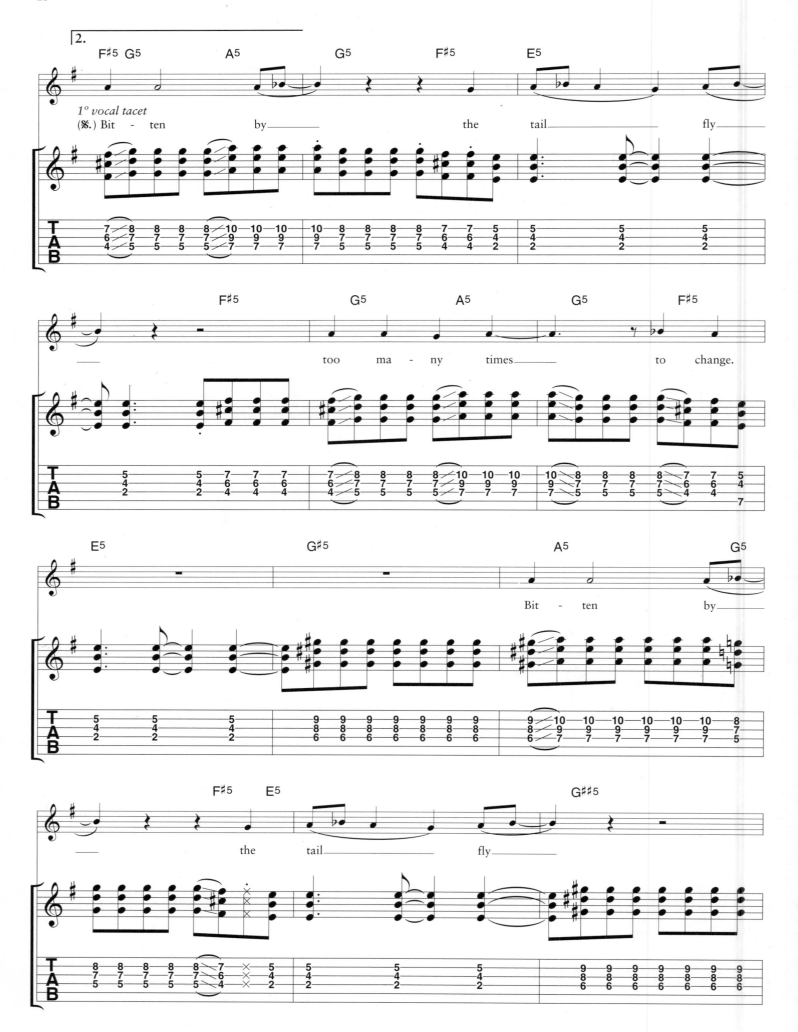

DON'T MIX YOUR DRINKS

Words and Music by Guy Garvey, Mark Potter, Craig Potter,
Richard Jupp and Pete Turner

Both Gtrs. Capo 3rd fret

Good— ad - vice,— sound— ad - vice—

(1.) why can't you be like— him, like— me.
(2.) you need to be like— this, like— me.

(1.) Look— what you could— ach - ieve.
(2.) tacet

w/delay   delay off

(1, 2.) I'm

mf

Chorus: Gm7   F   C   F

w/Fig. 2 *(Acous. Gtr. 1)*

com-ing cap in hand, beg-ging you to lis - ten.

Acous. Gtr. 2

C   F   C

Some - thing draws me in and

Gtr. 2: tacet

Fig. 2

Acous. Gtr. 1

Gm7   F   C   F

C   F   C

Instrumental:

Lyrics: I just— can't christ-en it   just— can't christ-en it.

(2.) Don't

Outro:

rall.

PRESUMING ED (REST EASY)

Words and Music by Guy Garvey, Mark Potter, Craig Potter,
Richard Jupp and Pete Turner

NEWBORN

Words and Music by Guy Garvey, Mark Potter, Craig Potter,
Richard Jupp and Pete Turner

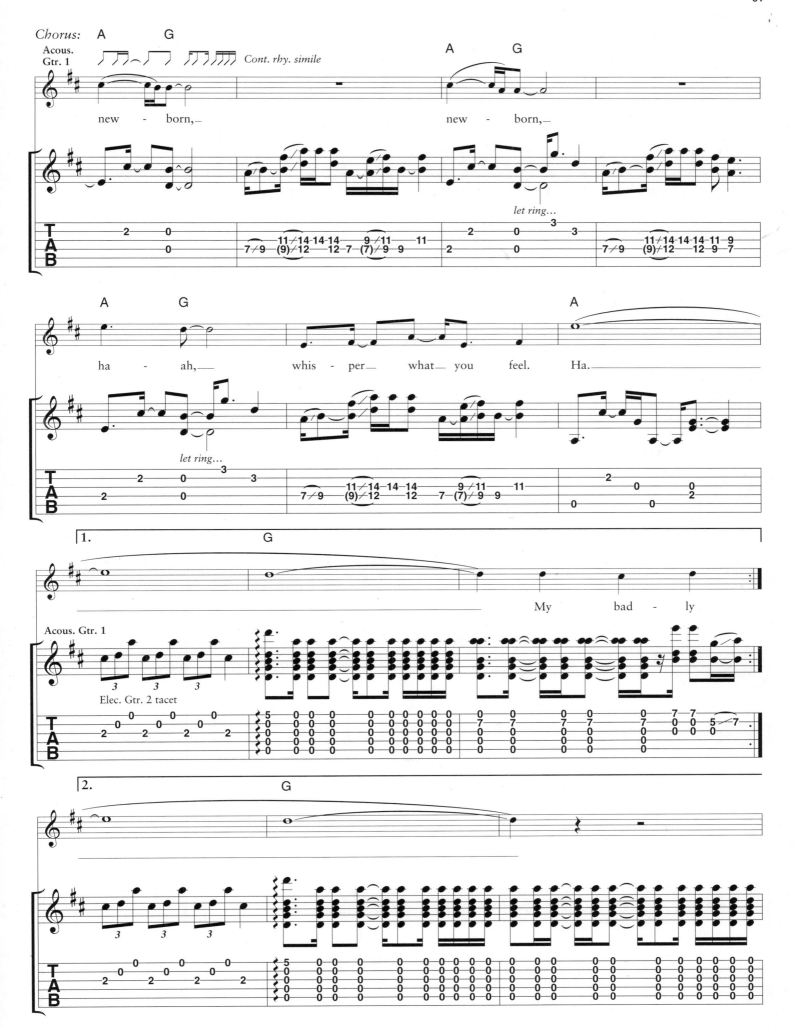

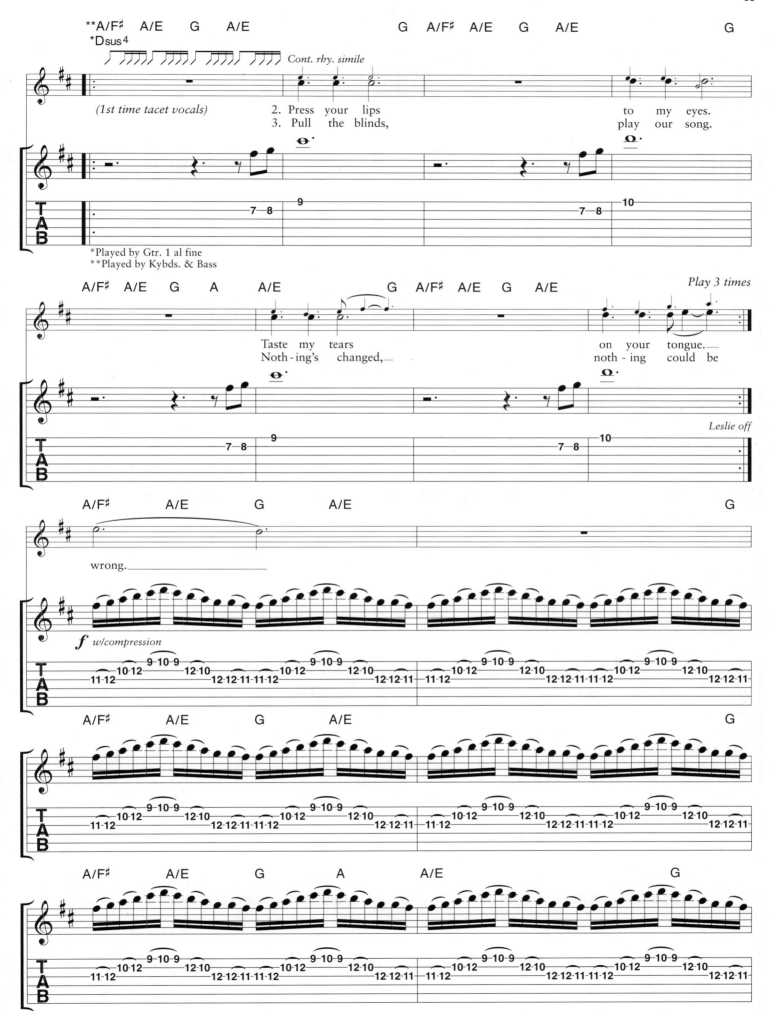

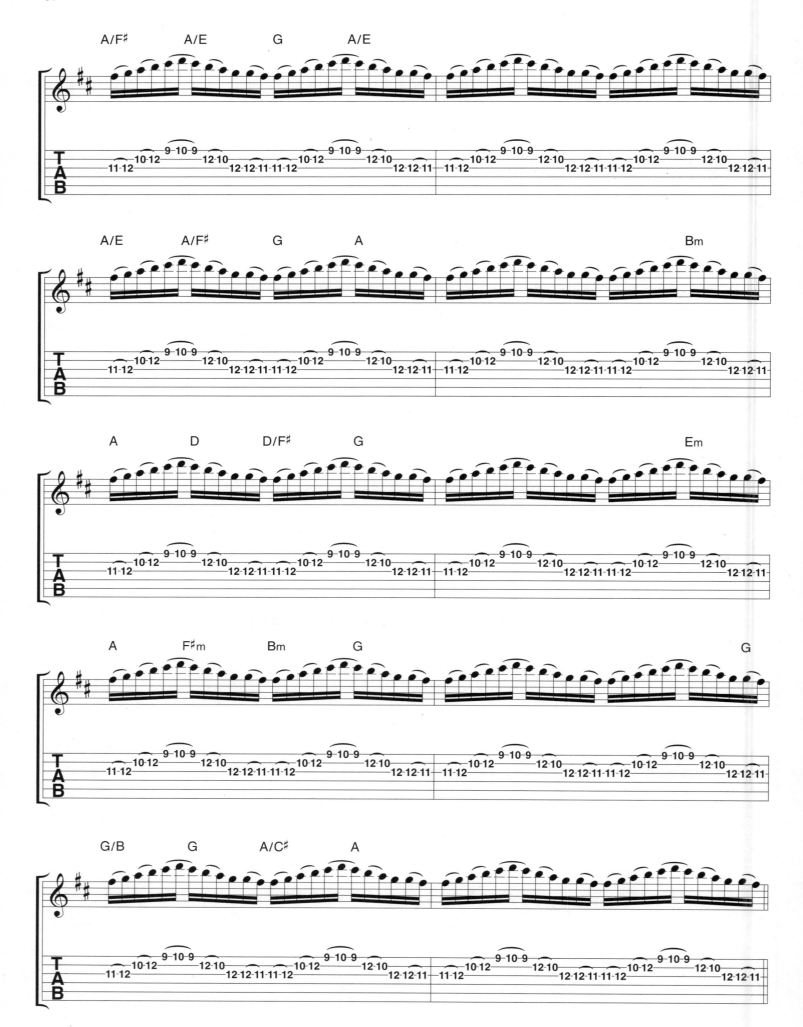

Elec guitar plays vocal pitch and 8vb

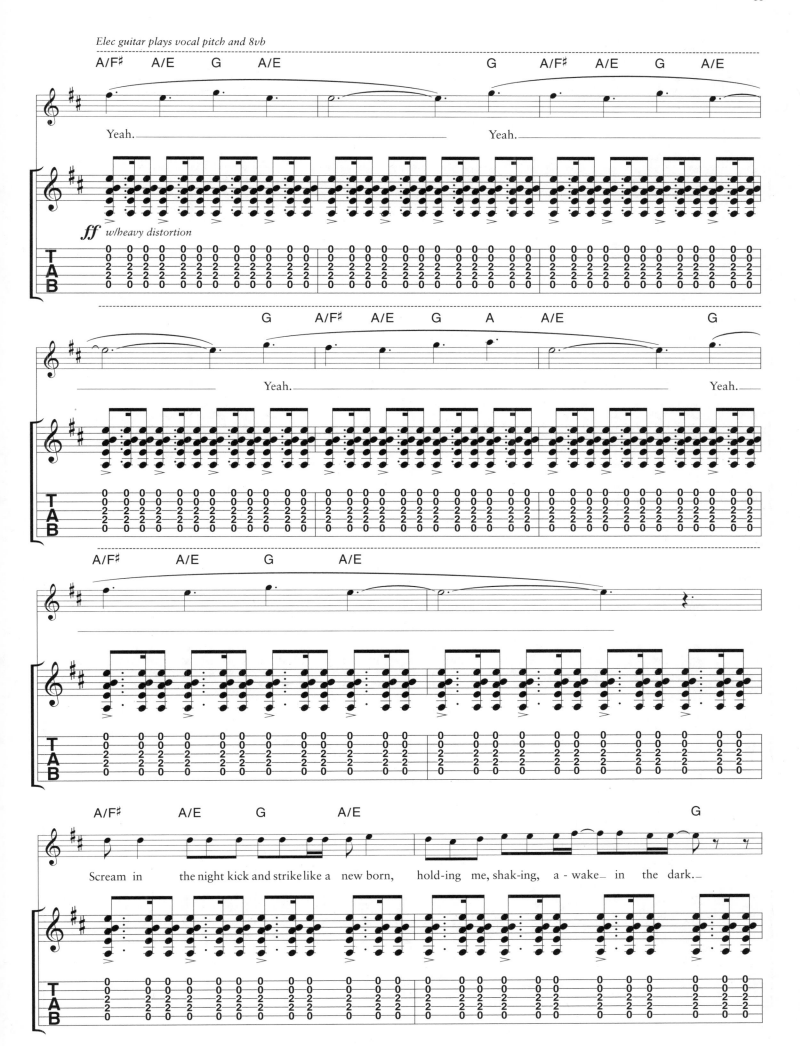

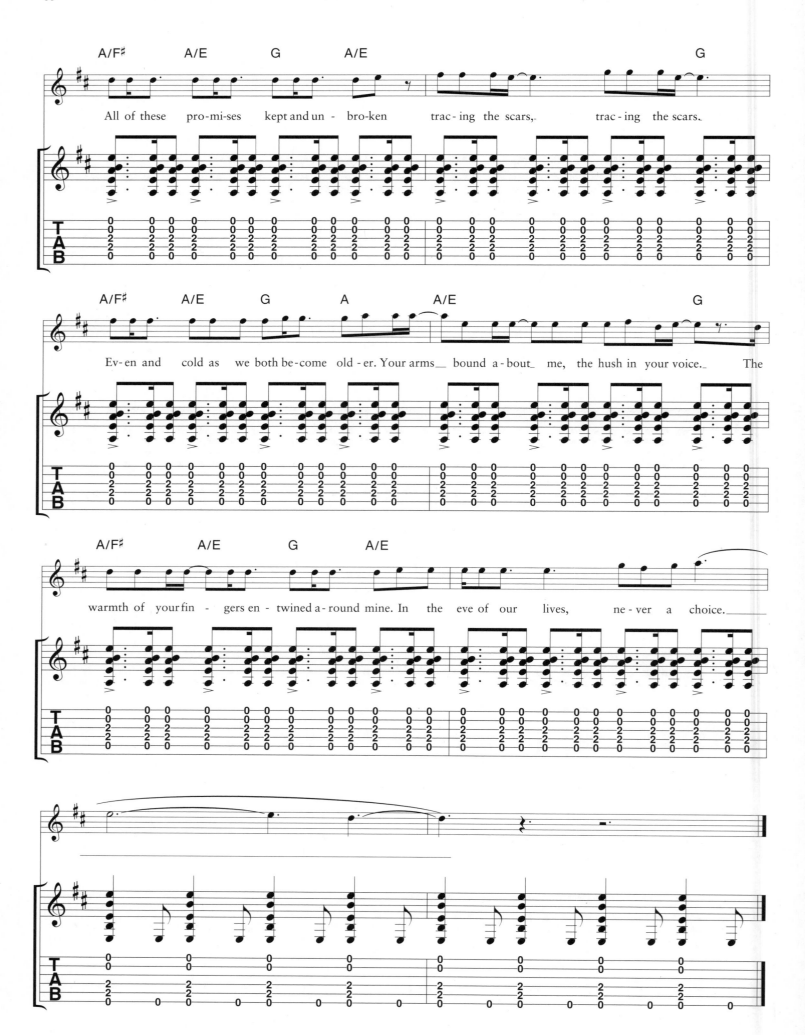

COMING SECOND

Words and Music by Guy Garvey, Mark Potter, Craig Potter,
Richard Jupp and Pete Turner

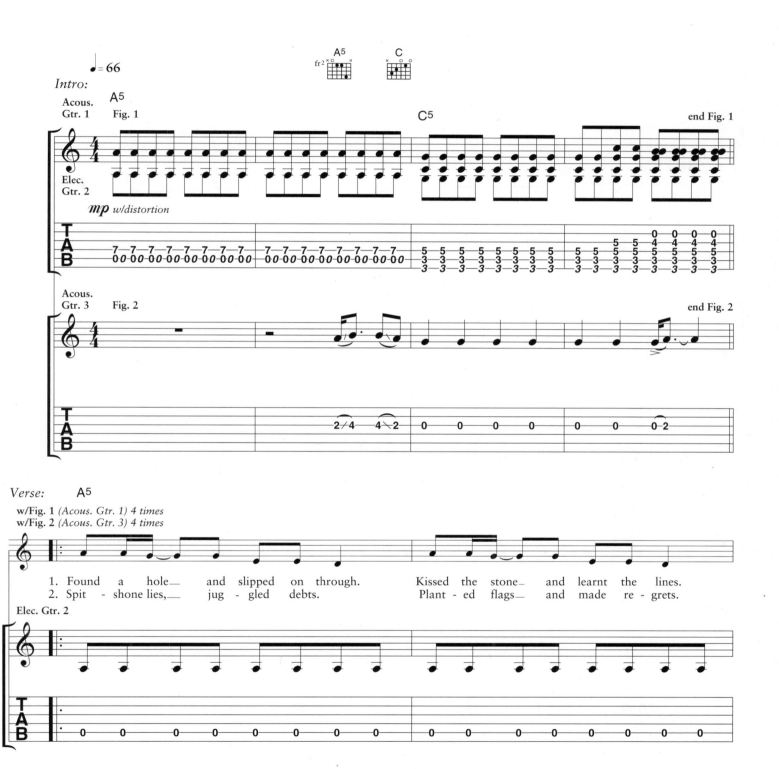

Chorus:

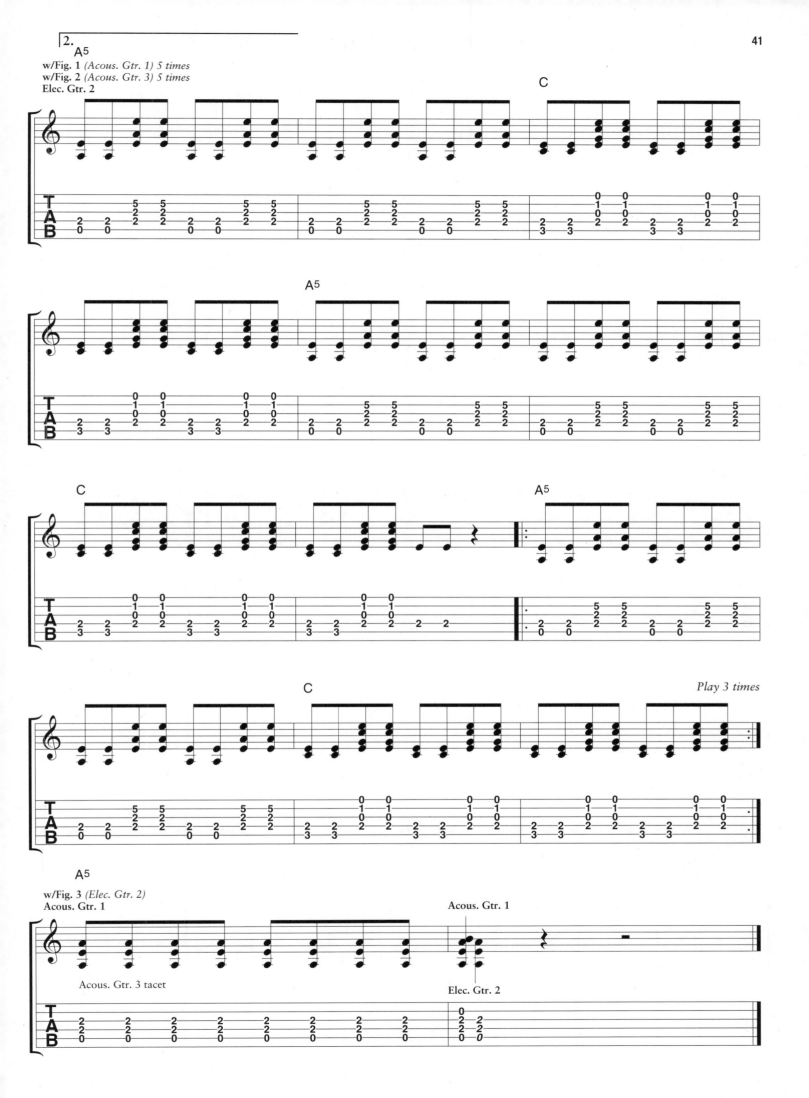

SCATTERED BLACK AND WHITES

Words and Music by Guy Garvey, Mark Potter, Craig Potter,
Richard Jupp and Pete Turner

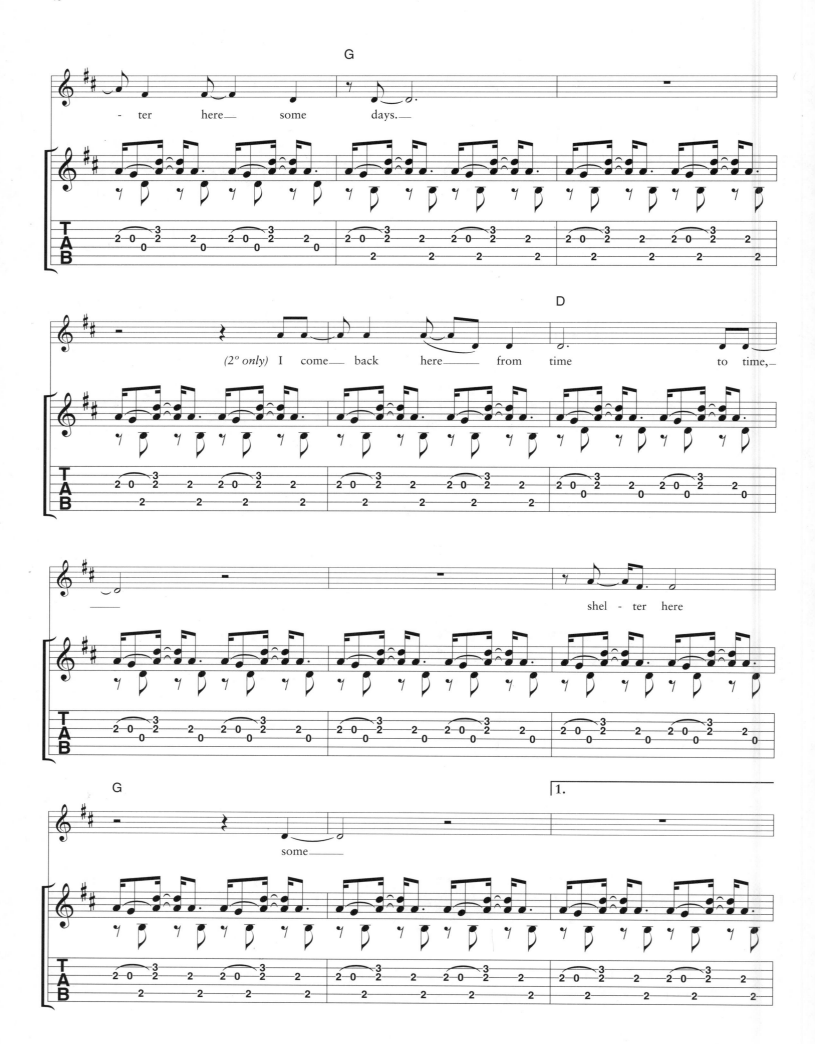

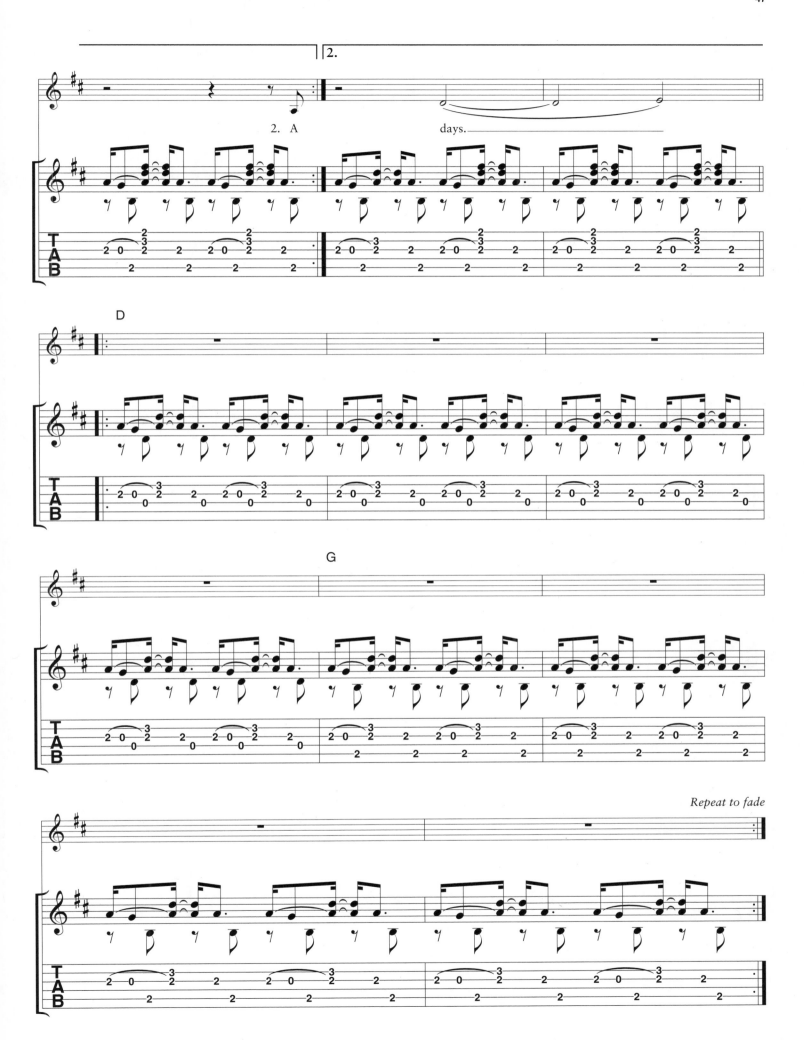

2. A

days.

D

G

Repeat to fade

CAN'T STOP

Words and Music by Guy Garvey, Mark Potter, Craig Potter,
Richard Jupp and Pete Turner

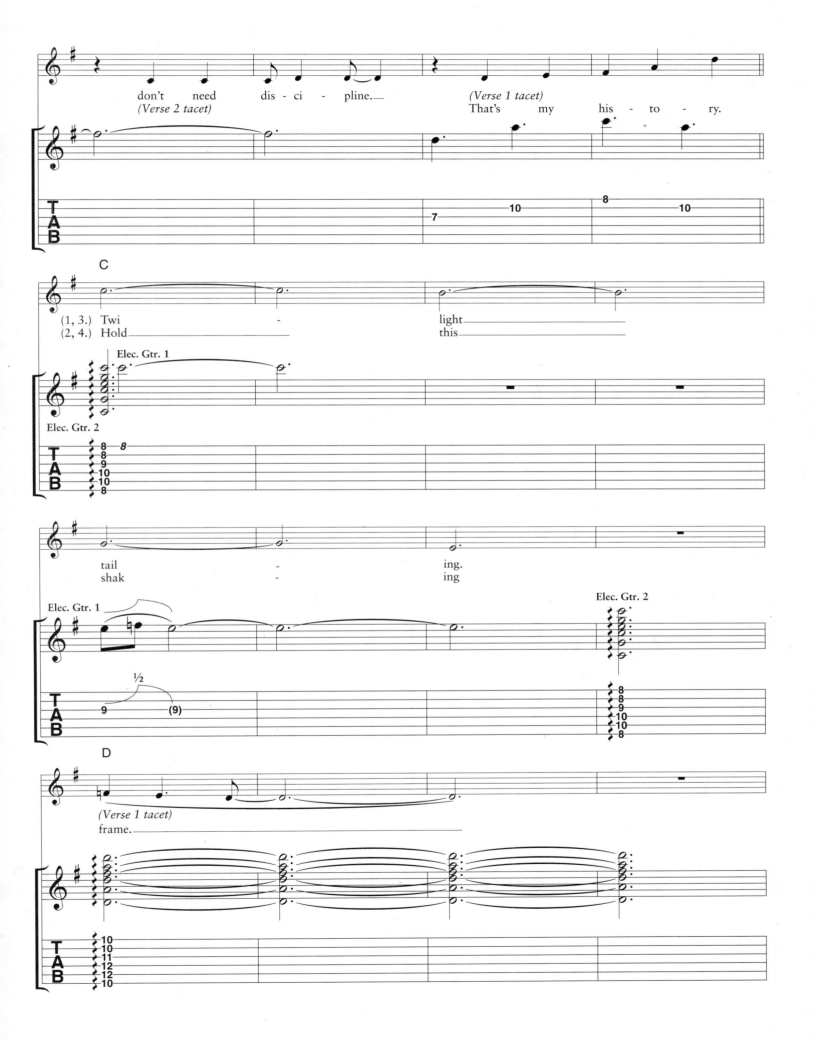

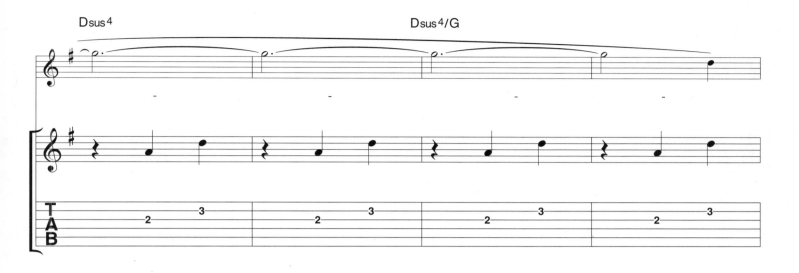

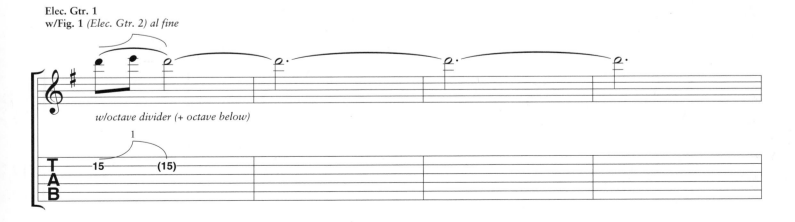

Verse 3:
What's your story? I
Want to listen. I
Can't fake pity. I
May not sympathise.
Twilights tailing

Verse 4:
Try my lies for size,
You might swallow them.
While I fantasise?
Try my lies for size.